For Matthew, Aiden, Audrey Anna, and Amelia Claire.
May music always bring magic to your lives.

Copyright ©2021 Charlene A. Ryan

First paperback edition October 2021

ISBN (paperback): 978-1-954041-12-7
ISBN (hardback): 978-1-954041-13-4

Published by Creative Sound Press
www.creativesoundpress.com
publishing@creativesoundpress.com

All book and cover art created with
oil on canvas by Charlene A. Ryan.
All rights reserved.

The Milk Crate Club

Charlene A. Ryan

The Milk Crate Club was an odd sort of club.

It didn't have a clubhouse.

It didn't have a secret code or handshake.

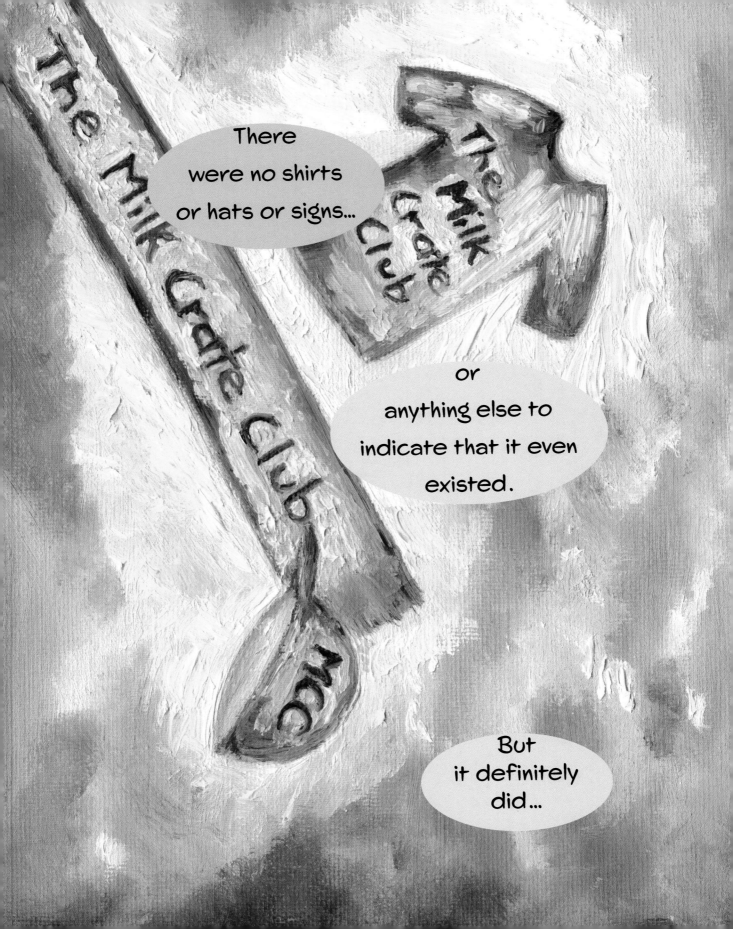

In truth, the only thing that club members seemed to have in common was a shared love of music.

And that, it seemed, was enough to make six very different kids...
the very best of friends.

It all started with Hannabelle. She was a singer. And a hummer. And she was almost always doing one or the other.

Hannabelle knew some other kids who loved music just as much as she did. And she thought it might be fun to bring them all together!

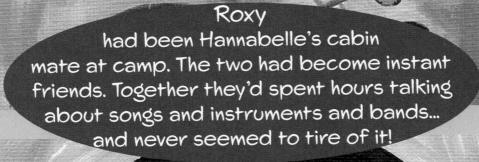

Roxy had been Hannabelle's cabin mate at camp. The two had become instant friends. Together they'd spent hours talking about songs and instruments and bands... and never seemed to tire of it!

Roxy played the guitar - electric guitar, mostly. And she loved rock music best of all.

She had been itching to play her guitar with a band, and was eager to get the club started!

Octavia
was Hannabelle's cousin.
She played the piano... every spare minute of the day

And while she enjoyed all kinds of music, what she loved most of all was playing with the sounds to make up her own songs.

Octavia had only ever played piano on her own. Hannabelle's idea to try playing together was so exciting!

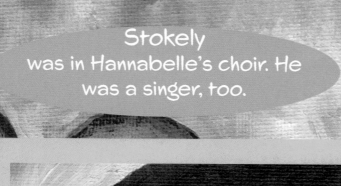

Stokely was in Hannabelle's choir. He was a singer, too.

And while he loved to sing, he LONGED to play the violin. He'd heard a man play it in the subway station and knew it was the instrument for him.

Stokely's mom had already found him a teacher and ordered his violin. He promised to show it to Hannabelle and the others as soon as it arrived.

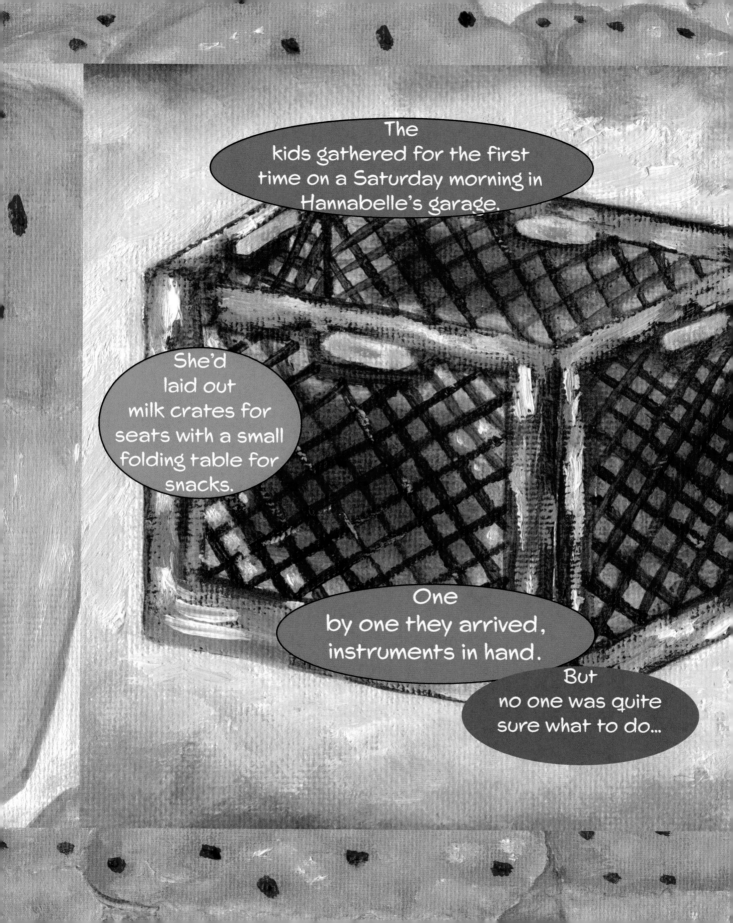

They all knew Hannabelle, but not each other.

So they ate their muffins and drank their juice in an awkward, uncertain kind of way.

It was a ROCKY start.

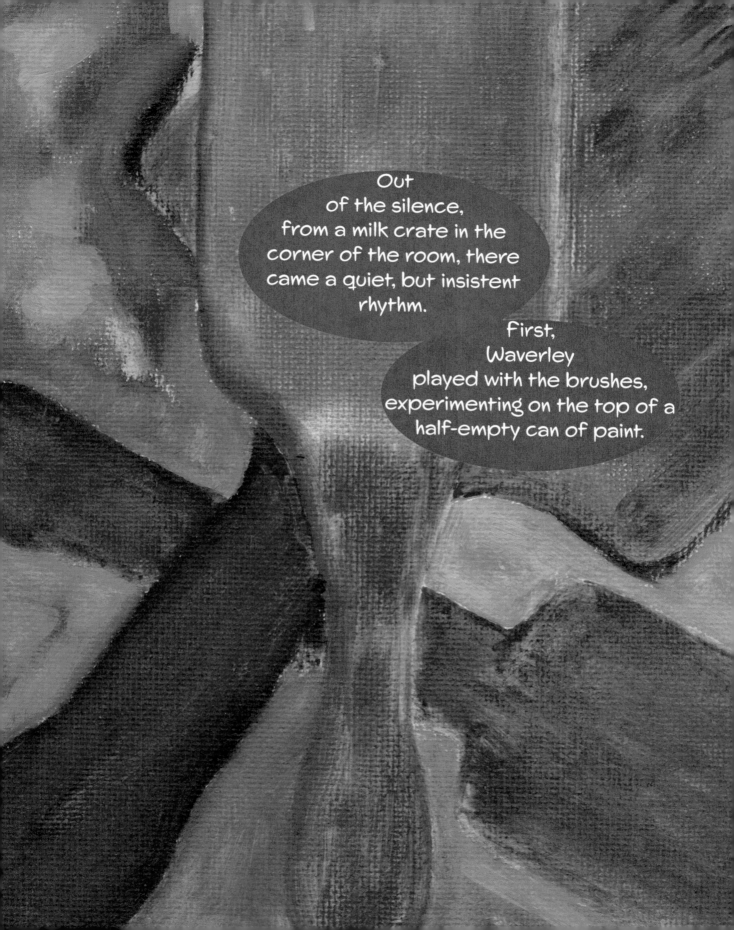

Roxy's foot began to tap.
She picked up her guitar. And, closing her eyes for a moment, she let the rhythm take hold...
then began to play, too.

The
energy
in the
room was
growing.

Waverley switched to his wooden drumsticks and the sound continued to build.

Hannabelle and Stokely looked at each other, their eyes wide with excitement.

Then Stokely joined in, singing a tune that rang out over the instruments.

At a loss for words, he used other sounds—la and da, oohh and dum.

And, strangely, it worked.

Ooh aah la-da dee-dum ooh-la-la-la

Scooty dooby oh la-la-la doby

Hannabelle was amazed at Stokely's creation, and soon followed his lead, adding her own voice to the mix.

The
music
grew and
grew, filling
the garage with
a spectacular
combination of
sounds never
heard before.

Together,
the kids were
creating their own
unique music right
then and there.
It felt like magic.

When Waverley swapped out his sticks for brushes, the volume diminished. Following suit, the other kids gradually got quieter and, one by one, dropped out. Soon they were back where they started, with a solitary rhythm on the paint cans.

As Waverley's drumming faded away, a **wondrous silence** filled the air.

Only
THIS was no ordinary
silence.

THIS
was the
silence that
follows a great
musical event—a
coming together of
musicians to create
something more than
they could make
alone.

Charlene A. Ryan is a musician,
painter, writer, and mom. She has
spent most of her life behind
an instrument and in front of an
audience of one kind or another.
To learn more about Charlene and
her work, visit charlenearyan.com

Other books by Charlene A. Ryan

Hannabelle's Butterflies

Katherine Lost

Up and Down Sounds

Big and Small Sounds

Sections of Sound

Made in the USA
Middletown, DE
06 November 2021